I Dig Freedom

Johnny Hart and Brant Parker

CORONET BOOKS
Hodder and Stoughton

Copyright © 1977 by News Group, Chicago, Inc.
First published in the United States of
America 1985 by Ballantine Books

Coronet edition 1987

British Library C.I.P.

Hart, Johnny
  I dig freedom.
  I. Title   II. Parker, Brant
  741.5'973   PN6727.H/

  ISBN 0-340-40791-3

Printed and bound in Great Britain for
Hodder and Stoughton Paperbacks, a
division of Hodder and Stoughton Ltd.,
Mill Road, Dunton Green, Sevenoaks,
Kent (Editorial Office: 47 Bedford
Square, London WC1B 3DP) by
Richard Clay Ltd, Bungay, Suffolk

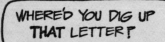

2-2

2·8

2-15

2·21

2-26

3-26

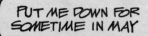

4-9

4-11

4-12

4·13

4:14

4-30

5-14

5-16

5-18

5-19

5·20

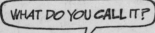

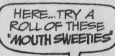

6·10

6·15

6-18

7-1

7-7

7-8